Kangaroo Red

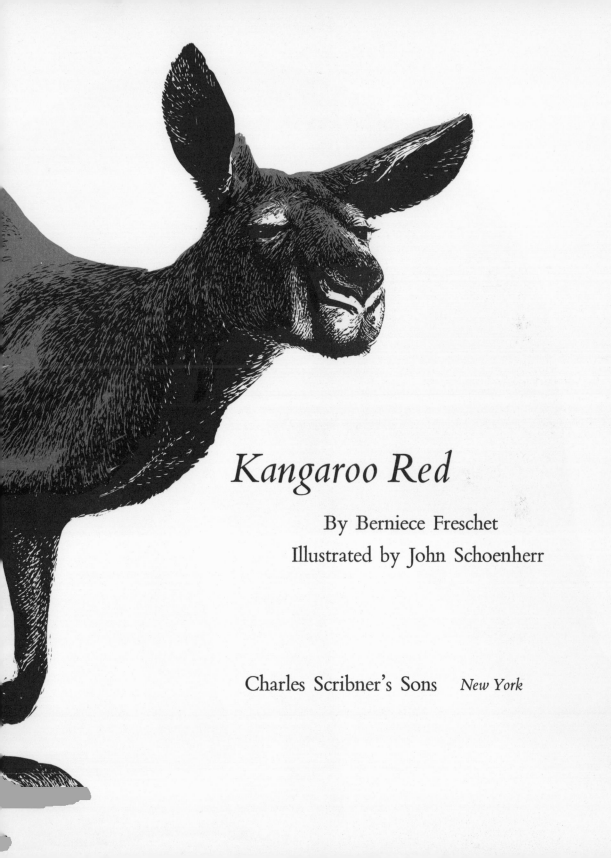

Kangaroo Red

By Berniece Freschet
Illustrated by John Schoenherr

Charles Scribner's Sons   *New York*

Kangaroo Red

THE GREAT OUTBACK, the Bush Country—this is what the people of Australia call the broad, dry and lonely interior of their land—the hundreds of thousands of square miles of rolling plains, red sand hills and bush-covered wilderness.

This land stretches as far as the eye can see—endless space, from horizon to horizon.

There is beauty here. The air is pure and crystal clear. The sky is a brilliant blue. The sun shines with an intensity that splashes the stark landscape in vivid reds, oranges and golds.

This is the land of vast herds of cattle and sheep—the land of the dingo and the "big red 'roo."

At sundown on an evening in April a family of kangaroos traveled along a worn, dusty trail toward water. It was a warm evening even though it was late autumn here, south of the equator.

The leader of the "mob," the "old man," came first, pushing his way through the dry grasses. The buck, a great red warrior, stood seven feet tall when he rose up on his toes and tail, and he weighed over two hundred pounds.

His forelimbs were short and muscular. He had long, powerful hindlimbs and a broad tapering tail which he used as a prop when he rose high up on his toes. His chest and stomach were the color of rich cream, his back and thighs a brick red.

Behind the old man trailed his fourteen wives. They were much smaller and lighter than he, and a blue-gray in color. Most of them carried "joeys" in their pouches, babies who ranged in age from a few hours to six months old.

They hopped slowly on all fours and several fat, young kangaroos played along the way. Chittering happily, they caught at each other's tails with their small hands or pulled at the shoots of grass beside the pathway.

The slow-moving caravan quickened its pace. The animals could smell and feel a change in the air and their noses twitched in excitement. Ahead was the billabong, their water hole, fed by an underground spring and by the rains during the wet season.

Palm trees, thick clumps of tropical plants and soft green grass grew all around. Tiny, delicate-petaled orchids twined through the grass and around the trunks of trees. Patches of clover filled the air with a sweet smell.

Here was a gift of nature, an oasis in an arid land of scrub brush and stunted trees.

With their large ears quivering the kangaroos moved up to the edge of the billabong to drink. They took their time, dipping their forelimbs up to their shoulders in the clear, cool water.

When the drink was finished they lingered in the cool of the evening to rest; and later they played in their lovely, moonlit garden.

Joey poked his head out of his mother's pouch. He began to grow restless in this dark, confined space, even though, at five months, he was not yet weaned from his mother.

He tried to push out farther. Scolding him with a "Chit, chit," his mother tightened the muscles of the pouch opening.

But the time had come when Joey wanted out.

He wiggled and squirmed and even kicked, until finally the young mother bent her head to scold more sternly. Joey reached up and catching her face with his small hands, he pressed his nose to hers. She began to lick his ears. And then, before he quite knew how it all came about, Joey found himself outside of the pouch, standing on the grass in the moonlight.

For a moment he stood alone on his long, slender hoppers. Wobbling unsteadily, he reached out for something to cling to. Finding nothing, he waited for courage to take his first step.

Another kangaroo hopped over, her baby close by. It was a little female almost the same age as Joey. The small kangaroos looked at each other curiously.

Except for their creamy white chests and stomachs, their fur was the color of blue smoke and soft as velvet. Their eyes were big and dark and their large ears quivered with excitement.

Joey moved unsteadily toward the little female, walking on all four feet. He rolled over on his back and for the first time saw his own feet. Cautiously, he stretched out one long hind leg as far as he could and then the other. How good it was to stretch his limbs and move freely about.

His mother and several of the other does, relieved of their babies for a short time, leaped away to wrestle and play in the

moonlight and to chase each other through the palm trees. Joey and the little female rolled happily together in the thick clover.

And then, in the short space of a heartbeat, all sound and movement stopped.

The kangaroos stood as still as if they had suddenly turned into stone.

Joey sensed that something was wrong and the next instant he heard and felt the thump of a tail whacking the ground. It was the old man signaling danger.

A flash of light shot out of the darkness, its beam catching the old man as he reared high up on his toes. The explosive sound of a rifle shattered the quiet of the night. Professional hunters had found the little band of kangaroos. They would sell the animals' hides for leather and their beautiful soft fur would be made into rugs and coats.

Another shot rang out. The red warrior's great body jerked and he fell crashing to the ground. Startled from their perches, shrieking birds flew out of the trees.

Terrified, the mother 'roos whose joeys were safe in their pouches, leaped out in all directions. Up, up—high into the air—twenty, thirty feet in a single bound and off at a speed of thirty miles an hour.

The other mothers frantically searched for their babies. The little female's mother came, found her, and fled.

Joey's small body trembled. What was happening? Where was his mother? He cried out for her.

He heard her answer, "Chut, Chut," and then she was there beside him. He dived headfirst into the pouch and, with a mighty bound, his mother leaped away. But precious seconds had been lost.

Just as Joey was beginning to feel safe once more, he heard the frightening sound again. His mother's body lurched violently. She stumbled. And then almost immediately she regained her balance and was bounding away.

But now there was a difference in her movements. Her jumps were not as smooth. Neither were they as high nor as far. Each time she hit the ground the jar shook Joey's body.

In a little while he heard his mother cry out. He felt her falling. She lay still.

The pouch muscles relaxed and Joey pulled himself out into the night. The little kangaroo was shaken from the fall. He nudged his mother's face, making small questioning sounds.

Joey called to her. He had not had his supper and he was hungry.
She did not answer.

Joey was alone in a strange and unfriendly world, and he was
afraid. He clutched his mother's fur in both hands and buried his
face in her chest. Finally he slept, holding tightly to her.

Glaring sunlight awakened him. For a moment he didn't
remember. And then it came back: the terror of the night, the feeling
of loneliness. He called to his mother. Again and again he called.
He waited. For a long while he waited until thirst forced him to go
in search of water.

He started off on his slender, wobbly legs. The tangled grass tripped him and he often stumbled and fell. Accustomed to the dark and quiet of his mother's pouch, he was frightened by the fierce light of the sun and the whine of the wind.

Stones and twigs bruised his tender feet and his baby muscles soon become stiff and sore. Joey wanted to rest, but his need for water drove him on.

The time came when he stumbled, fell and could not rise again. He closed his eyes to shut out the blinding light of the sun.

Half a mile away a fox had seen the little kangaroo and came creeping silently toward him.

And then Joey heard a familiar thump, thump, thump. He struggled and pushed until finally he sat up so he could see over the tops of the wavering grasses.

The fox crouched low.

A mother kangaroo came bounding his way. In the confusion of the night one of the does had been unable to find her baby. She had come back to look for him.

The doe saw Joey and leaped eagerly toward him. He sat up as high as he could. Holding his small hands out in front of him, Joey chittered feebly.

The doe looked him over, smelled him and then, appearing to lose interest, she started away.

Joey called out to her. His big, dark eyes and all of his small self pleaded for her to stay.

She stopped and moved her head from side to side, as though making sure no other baby kangaroo was in sight.

Joey called again.

And then she turned and bounded forward, hopping straight for him.

After Joey had suckled milk until his stomach was full, he slept. When he awoke many hours later, most of the stiff and sore spots were gone.

At first he was confused. Where was he? Not where the glaring hot light beat down, but safe once more inside a dark pouch. He knew by the smell that it was not his mother's pouch, but it felt very comforting.

He poked his head outside and looked around. Seven does and five young kangaroos lay in shallow nests, scooped out hollows in the earth under the shade of a tall gum tree. They were all that remained of his scattered family, and they had returned to their home in the grove of gum trees.

They liked to stay here during the hottest part of the day, resting and chewing their cuds and hopping to the water hole in the cool of the evening.

When the sun dropped below the horizon and the shadows of twilight moved slowly across the great plains, the kangaroos grew restless. It was time to go to water, but they waited. Where was the old man who had always led them?

Two of the does hopped away in the direction of the water hole, but when the others did not follow they returned.

Some of the kangaroos grazed. Some lay back down in their nests. And some sat on their haunches, propping themselves on their broad, muscular tails.

Without the old man they seemed puzzled as to what to do next. They spent the night moving restlessly about.

In the morning, thirst drove them to search for water. They wandered north, away from the familiar but now dangerous billabong. They stopped often to graze.

Occasionally Joey stuck his head out of his foster mother's pouch to see what was going on. He had not yet forgotten his fright and so he was not as eager to leave the pouch now as he had been before.

Late in the afternoon the 'roos came to a fence strung with wire and they crawled under it. They were on a huge cattle and sheep station, and here they found a pond. They had barely satisfied their thirst when two boundary riders galloped toward them, shouting and cracking their stockwhips in the air.

The kangaroos bounded away. The fence loomed up in front of them and this time they did not stop to crawl under, but with long graceful leaps they soared high into the air and over the top of it.

The kangaroos recognized these men as enemies. For each year ranch hands kill thousands of kangaroos because they compete with the cattle and sheep for the scarce grass. However, this time the cowboys did not shoot at them, and so the small band continued north.

Sometimes Joey hopped along with the others. Now he was
beginning to drink less milk and eat more grass.

In a few days the kangaroos came to an even more desolate and
arid country. Here for many miles they crossed a large flat area of
dry, caked mud. Now when Joey poked his head out of the pouch
he often saw snakes and lizards wriggling out of the way.

Once he saw a monitor lizard, almost five feet long, basking in the morning sun. As the kangaroos came close, the big creature ambled away, his body and tail moving slowly from side to side and his long blue tongue flicking in and out. All that day Joey stayed inside the pouch.

Gradually the land began to change into rolling plains of dry, spiny grass that gleamed and shimmered in the sunlight.

Once they came across a band of wild camels. These were the descendants of the camels in the Afghan camel trains that at one time were used to cross the dry desert regions.

Early one morning Joey saw a flock of emus, strange-looking birds grazing on the plains. Some of them stood six feet tall. Their bodies were covered with drooping grayish-brown feathers.

The birds raised their long graceful necks and watched as the little band hopped close. Then, suddenly startled, they raced away. The big birds could not fly, but they could run very fast.

They often saw wallabies, the small kangaroos. These ranged from about half the size of the big red 'roos, down to the tiny rat kangaroo which stood only fourteen inches tall.

Hardly a day went by that high overhead in the sky there wasn't a pair of hungry wedge-tailed eagles dipping and gliding on silent wings. They were waiting and watching to see if one of the young kangaroos might become separated from his mother.

After traveling for many days, late one afternoon the small band came to a quiet river shaded by tall eucalyptus trees and spreading boughs of acacia. Rushes grew along the river banks and sunlight filtered down through the treetops, making rippling patterns of light that danced across the water.

Brilliant-feathered parrots, budgies and lovebirds made the air gay with chatter and the skies flash with color.

For several days the kangaroos rested on the banks of the river. On hot afternoons they waded into the water. It was here, beside the quiet river, that a strong and handsome young buck found the band and claimed it for his own.

Once again they had an old man to lead, and now they were content to stay here, close to the water.

Joey was growing. He was over seven months old and no longer drank his foster mother's milk but preferred to nibble the tender shoots of grass.

In place of baby chubbiness, hard muscles had begun to bunch in his forelimbs and back. When he stretched high, the top of his head reached almost to his mother's shoulders. Now he must look after himself. For already his foster mother carried a tiny, blind, naked, new baby in her pouch.

Like many young animals, Joey was very curious. He had to see, taste and smell everything. But in the manner of kangaroos he was also timid and shy; and because of his frightening experience with the hunters, Joey was especially timid.

There were several young kangaroos for Joey to play with, but his favorite companion was the little blue female that he had first met beside the billabong at the oasis. He would come to her and, standing high on his toes and the tip of his tail, he would make several stiff, bounding side-hops, inviting her to play. Chittering, little Blue would romp off, leading him on a fast chase through the trees.

One dusky evening the two young kangaroos watched together on the bank as a herd of water buffalo lounged in the river. All they could see of the big animals were their dark snouts and backward-sweeping horns.

A chunky young buffalo climbed out of the water and stared at the two young kangaroos. Head lowered, he made a sudden playful charge and butted Joey.

Caught unawares, Joey was sent sprawling to the ground. Timidly, he scrambled away but kept a watchful eye on his attacker.

The young buffalo liked the game. He turned and charged little Blue. He sent her somersaulting across the grass, chittering with fright.

Quickly Joey drew himself high up on his toes and tail. Bouncing in stiff little side-hops, he danced in front of the enemy. "Chut!" he cried, inviting the buffalo to fight. "Chut!"

The buffalo lowered his head for another charge. But the next instant he let out a bellow of surprise and pain.

Clutching the enemy's neck with both hands, Joey drove a well-aimed kick hard into the buffalo's side. With his hind foot he raked his long sharp toenail across the thick hide, tearing out a hunk of skin and hair.

The buffalo struggled to escape.

Joey kicked out again.

Bellowing for his mother, the victim leaped for safety.

Joey stood erect, his chest out and his arms swinging. Those were his first fighting kicks, and now he knew something of the great power in his forelimbs and legs. Never again would he be quite so timid.

When Joey was one year old he stood five feet tall and weighed close to seventy pounds. He was beginning to shed his blue coat for the yellowish-orange fur of the male yearling. Even though he looked shaggy and unkempt, he already showed promise of becoming as magnificent a kangaroo buck as his father had been.

Now in play he boxed with other young males. They were practicing for the battles that would one day come when they challenged the old man for rule of the mob and, later, the bloody fights that must be fought to defend and hold their own harem of does.

At two years Joey was a handsome, strong young buck weighing two hundred pounds. His coat was red and shiny. Now when he boxed with the other young males his blows were harder and not always playful.

The day came when the leader of the mob looked upon Joey as a rival. He did not like the young buck's friendship with the little blue doe. One morning the old man rose high up on his tail and toes, stuck out his chest and hopped stiffly around Joey. It was a challenge to battle. "Chut!" he called.

Joey was ready and eager to fight. "Chut!" he answered. He rose and bounced forward to meet the old man.

They grappled, each struggling for a hold.

The leader suddenly lashed out with his forearms. Swift, jolting blows shook Joey down to the very tips of his toes.

He fought back, but he was not yet full-grown and no match for the older and stronger big red 'roo who gave no mercy.

The fight was soon over and Joey was driven from the mob. He stayed within sight of the family, for he was not yet ready to wander the plains alone.

He was not by himself for long, however, for in the days that followed, one by one, other vanquished young males joined him.

Some of the young bucks left the area and went in search of other old men to challenge. But Joey would not leave without little Blue.

Soon it was September and spring. The bush country became a wonderland of color. Wild flowers grew everywhere. Acacia trees

burst out in bright yellow blossoms. The scarlet and white flowers of the tall, eucalyptus trees filled the air with their spicy fragrance. Birds flitted busily from bough to bough, their call-songs ringing through the skies.

From a lonely distance Joey watched the little blue doe and the other kangaroos resting and playing beside the river. He wanted to be with them, but whenever he came too close the old man would rear up and threaten him. Twice more he fought the leader and each time he was driven away again.

From across the water came the loud, mocking laughter of the kookaburra bird.

Joey stubbornly stayed within sight of the mob.

Spring drifted into summer. Overhead the sun blazed down and the grass was yellow and dry. Still Joey stayed on.

And then one day a great black cloud rolled over the distant hills and with it the smell of smoke.

The animals of the bush country instantly sensed mortal danger —bush fire!

The kangaroos sniffed the strong smell of smoke and their noses twitched in fear.

Great clouds blackened the sky. Yellow tongues of flame licked down from the hills and through the dry grasses. Terrified animals raced side by side.

Close to Joey bounded the little blue doe.

Soon the sky grew even darker. However, now the darkness was not from the clouds of smoke alone but from great, black thunderheads that rolled aloft.

Lightning flashed and thunder boomed and rain poured down. The wet season of late summer had come to the plains.

The kangaroos greeted the rains with dancing leaps of joy. By the time the storm had put out the bush fire the mob was scattered far and wide. The little blue doe followed Joey.

He led her south—away from the river, away from the old man.

Not only had the rains stopped the fire from spreading but "the wet" brought new life to the bush country. The great plains became a carpet of green as new grass sprang up almost overnight.

Billabongs overflowed. Dry lakes became real lakes and once again rivers filled and flowed swiftly to the sea.

For many days the two young kangaroos traveled south. During the hottest part of the afternoon they stopped to rest under whatever shade they could find.

As they traveled further inland, the landscape began to change and faint memories stirred within Joey—memories of a dusty path through tall wavering grass, of palm trees and clover and pale moonlight. Sometimes he and little Blue would stay for many days where the grass was good and water was near. But always the memories of the desert oasis and the clear-running billabong where he had first seen the little blue doe urged him on.

Instinct was drawing Joey back to the place where he had been born. And so for many weeks the kangaroos pushed on, always traveling south.

When Joey was three and a half years old he was in his prime, a fine specimen of strength and grace. The muscles in his arms and back rippled under his coat of glossy chestnut-colored fur. He stood over seven feet tall and weighed 240 pounds. He was every bit as brave and as great a red 'roo as his father had been.

One night, as the two 'roos lay sleeping beneath a large gum tree, the howl of a dingo dog sounded across the plains.

Joey was instantly awake, his sensitive ears flicking nervously, listening.

Another howl pierced the night air. Then another. Nearer this time, for the dingo pack had caught the scent of the kangaroos and came running fast.

Joey and little Blue jumped up and bounded away. Their feet thudded rhythmically against the earth as great flying leaps kept them airborne most of the time.

They would not be able to keep up this fast a pace for long. They were beginning to tire when suddenly an eight-foot wire mesh fence loomed before them, barring their escape.

Gathering speed, they made straight for the tall barrier. Twenty feet from the fence they hit the ground and hurled themselves into the air, pulling their powerful legs close to their bodies.

Up they flew. Up! Up! Over the top of the fence. Then down the other side to safety.

The angry dingoes leaped high against the fence but fell back. They raged as the kangaroos disappeared into the darkness.

When Joey and little Blue were far enough away to feel safe they stopped to rest. The moon slid from behind a dark cloud, silhouetting the fringed tops of palm trees a short distance away.

Joey raised his head and looked at the trees. He sat up, his nose twitching with excitement. He hopped forward down a dusty, familiar pathway. Little Blue followed.

Soon they were among the palm trees and tropical plants. Sweet clover grew beside a bubbling spring and tiny delicate-petaled orchids twined through the grasses and around the trunks of trees.

Joey and little Blue moved up to the edge of the billabong and drank of the clear, cool water.

Two stray does came from behind a clump of plants and hopped to the stream. Shyly the animals touched noses as though welcoming each other.

For the first time in many weeks Joey was free of the restless yearning that had driven him for so long. Now he was truly an old man with a family of his own to take care of.

The kangaroos leaped away, to chase each other through the palm trees and to wrestle and play in the moonlight.